TRY THIS!

BIZARRE BIOLOGY EXPERIMENTS FOR THE MAD SCIENTIST IN YOU

KAREN ROMANO YOUNG
PHOTOGRAPHS BY MATTHEW RAKOLA

NATIONAL GEOGRAPHIC

WASHINGTON, D.C.

BIZARREBIOLOGY

Just below the surface of everyday life, there lie riddles. Here are a few ways to dig down to the root of some mysteries about ourselves, our pets, and other animals.

SORTING THE TRASH

DOG BED SOCK I.D.

PHONY SMILES

RIGHTY LEFTY

CAT IQ
TEST

MAKE
FOOTPRINT
CASTS

DOGS AND
POINTING

7·8
Hard boiled

EGG TRICK

NEARSIGHTED
HOOPS

PHONY SMILES

Smiles: fake or real?

CONCEPTS

INTERPRETATION, OBSERVATION, TECHNOLOGY, BEHAVIOR

HOW LONG IT TAKES
two or more days

WHAT YOU NEED
camera (the one on a smartphone is fine)
computer or computer tablet to show your photographs on
optional: You can also print out photographs and show the prints to your subjects.
three actors
as many subjects as you wish
optional: a partner to film while you interview your subjects

How often do you really smile, and how often do you fake it? Often enough to be able to tell the difference when other people do it? This study lets you see how well people read others.

QUESTION THIS!

• Researchers trying to get better at reading facial expressions sometimes watch video with the sound off. Why would this help?

• Are some people better than others at fake smiles?

• How about those jokes? How can you explain why different people respond to them in different ways? Did your actors agree with you about which joke was funniest?

WHAT TO DO

DAY ONE:

1 PREPARE your photographs. Photograph each actor separately. For each actor, do the following:

a. Select three jokes. Try to find one that is really hilarious, one that's kind of lame, and one that is somewhere in the middle.

b. Take four photographs of each actor, one of his response to each of the three jokes, plus one more. For the last photograph, ask the actor to smile as if he were hearing a hilarious joke.

DAY TWO:

2 YOU'LL HAVE 12 photographs, four for each of your three actors. Show them to your subjects. Ask them to guess real (R) and fake (F) smiles for each actor. The score sheet might look like this when filled in. The response column is for the subject's assessment of the actor's four smiles.

	Actor 1: Wyatt	response	Actor 2: Brandon	response	Actor 3: Niyanna	response
Knock knock joke	Real	F	R	F	F	F
Slide joke	Real	F	F	F	R	F
Elephant joke	Real	R	R	F	R	R
Fake smile	Fake	F	F	R	F	R

"This is hard! Is a laugh the same as a smile?"
—Bailey

WHAT TO EXPECT People will probably be pretty good judges of real and fake smiles.

WHAT'S GOING ON? Researchers have learned that a facial expression is actually made up of microexpressions, fleeting glimpses of a subject's true feelings. A still photograph may provide a quick, focused look that clues you in to how genuine each smile is.

OUR JOKES

How does the man in the moon cut his hair? Eclipse it.
Why did the cookie cry? Because his mother was a wafer so long.
Why are all the frogs around here dead? Because they keep croaking.
What happened when the butcher backed into his meat grinder? He got a little behind in his work.*
What did one hat say to the other? You stay here. I'll go on ahead.
What's brown and sticky? A stick.

* Nobody laughed at this joke.

SORTING THE TRASH

What if you didn't take out the trash?

HOW LONG IT TAKES
two days

WHAT YOU NEED
a kitchen scale
a cloth tote bag
a notebook
optional: camera

Sick of taking out the trash? Maybe the problem isn't taking it out; maybe the trouble is how much goes in. Here's a tip: reduce, reuse, or recycle. What can an individual do? Start by finding out how much trash you send to the dump, then figure out how to dump less.

WHAT TO DO

DAY ONE:

1 FOR ONE WHOLE DAY, throw nothing out. Keep your tote bag with you. Put all your trash in the tote bag. Follow these rules:

a. You can't use the garbage cans at home or school. You can't use public garbage cans. You can't use ANY garbage cans.

b. You can't give garbage to somebody else to throw out for you, flush trash down the toilet, or litter.

c. You CAN recycle, compost, incinerate (with adult help), and donate usable items to charity.

d. You have to keep any trash you generate within five feet (1.5 meters) of you.

2 AT THE END of the day, take everything out of your bag. Weigh it, categorize it, and photograph it.

DAY TWO:

3 REPEAT THIS experiment, using what you learned on Day One.

WHAT TO EXPECT On the second day, you'll produce less trash than the first.

WHAT'S GOING ON? Awareness of where trash comes from can keep you from making choices that lead to trash. Awareness of how trash might be useful can reduce the amount of stuff you throw out.

QUESTION THIS!

• Make a note of each thing you toss. Why did you have it in the first place? Was there a way to cut down on trash with this item?

• Are there common characteristics in most of the items you throw out? For instance, does paper predominate?

• What rules could or should communities make to reduce trash?

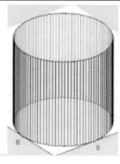

BONUS

PENCIL OF POWER

Here's something to do with that soda can you're stuck carrying around.

Stand on a can and it won't collapse. Put light pressure with a pencil point on the side of the can, and it will crumble.

QUESTION Why does this happen? We asked physicist Dr. Todd Baker at the University of Georgia, the professor behind askthephysicist.com.

ANSWER "Imagine the can to be made up of many thin sticks (pictured left); I will suppose there are 100 sticks and your weight is 100 pounds (45.4 kg). Each stick must therefore hold up 1 pound (.5 kg). If the stick is perfectly straight, it is able to support 1 pound, but if it gets the slightest kink in it, it will not and will quickly fold. But that stick is attached to the sticks on either side of it, so if it folds, it will drag its neighbors with it and they will drag theirs and the whole can will fail." Thanks, Dr. Baker!

RIGHTY LEFTY

Which side is dominant?

HOW LONG IT TAKES
thirty minutes for each subject

WHAT YOU NEED
You'll test your subject in an area that includes
a staircase
a ball
an empty paper towel tube
a picture hanging on the wall
paper
pen
chalk
cup of water
scissors
small box with mystery object inside (your choice)

Babies can show hand dominance even before they're born. Other preferences develop as we grow and change. Nevertheless, you might be surprised at some of the preferences you find in yourself.

1k

WHAT TO DO

1 PLAN YOUR TEST. You'll be testing whether each subject prefers her right or left hand, foot, eye, and ear. You will ask her to do a series of tasks, while observing her to see which hand, foot, eye, or ear she uses. So set up the tasks and plan a route for the subject to follow. Here are the tasks:

a. Sit at a table. Take a sip from the cup of water. (Which hand is used to lift the cup to the mouth?)

b. While still at the table, draw a spiral on a sheet of paper. (Which hand is used? In what direction does the spiral's opening face, left or right? This could indicate dominant eye.)

c. While still at the table, look through the paper tube at an object on the wall. (To which eye does the subject raise the tube?)

d. Look at the same object without the tube. Now put one thumb up to block the object. Close one eye, then the other. Can you still see the object with the left eye closed? How about with the right eye closed? (Which eye blocks the object?)

e. Pick up a sheet of paper with a small hole (the size of a penny) cut out of it. Holding the paper at arm's length, look through the hole at the object on the wall. Now bring the paper closer to your face while keeping your eye on the object. (To which eye does the subject bring the hole?)

f. Pick up a small box with a mystery object inside. Hold it to the ear to try to identify what's inside the box. (Which ear does the subject bring the box to?)

g. Whisper to your subject. (Observe which ear she turns toward you or cups to hear what you say.)

h. Stand up. Step on a penny that's been left on the floor. (Which foot is used?)

i. Step over a chalk line on the floor. (Which foot steps over first?)

j. Kick a ball. (Which foot is used?) How about a running kick? (You'll likely take off on the nondominant foot to get the dominant foot in position to kick.)

k. Walk up the stairs. (Which foot steps up first?)

l. Stand with your feet hip-distance apart. Lean forward until you go off balance and put one foot out to keep from falling. (Which foot do you put out?)

Note: Matt, our photographer, suggested we add this last one about falling. And we found something surprising: Most of us put our nondominant foot forward. We wondered if it was like running up to kick a ball—you take off with the nondominant foot in order to get the dominant foot in position to walk forward.

2 CREATE A CHECKLIST to help you with your observations. It might look like this:

Subject	Task	Right	Left
Patsy	a. sip water	X	
	b. draw spiral		X
	c. paper tube	X	

WHAT TO EXPECT Most subjects will show clear preference for one side or the other, but some will be different for hands and feet, and others will use left and right equally.

WHAT'S GOING ON? People have dominant parts of their bodies overall, but also for different tasks. There are different scientific theories for why this is so, but most scientists agree that it has to do with the brain. The brain has two halves, and each half has different functions. In humans, who use language, the half of the brain most associated with language is the left hemisphere. In 70 to 95 percent of humans, the left hemisphere controls language. Since the left hemisphere of the brain controls the right side of the body, most humans are right-dominant, too. Even so, handedness isn't absolute. Some people are completely righties, but may be lefties for sports or may prefer their left eye or ear. Others use left and right almost equally. Others are completely left-dominant.

QUESTION THIS!

- How many subjects would you need to test to replicate the percentage above?

- What can you learn by looking at handedness in individual subjects?

- What can you learn by testing yourself?

DOG BED SOCK I.D.

Can you identify your dog by his smell?

>> **HOW LONG IT TAKES**
three to four days

>> **WHAT YOU NEED**
access to the dog beds of four dogs
besides your own
five socks
five quart-size (liter-size) Ziploc bags,
labeled 1 to 5
permanent marker or stick-on labels

Some senses get more attention than others. Sure you know your dog—or your brother—by looks. You can probably identify either one by the sound of his voice, too. But what about smell? Try this with dogs, cats, or people. (We show the dog test here!)

WHAT TO DO

1 FIRST, GET THE cooperation of four dog owners. They will need to help prepare the experiment and act as subjects.

2 EACH HUMAN SUBJECT gets one clean sock and Ziploc bag. She places the sock in her dog's bed, leaving it there for 48 hours—two days and nights. During this time the dog should sleep with or on the sock.

3 AFTER THE 48 HOURS are over, all the human subjects should place the socks in Ziploc bags and meet at your house.

4 ASK THE HUMAN subjects to wait in another room while you number the bags with a permanent marker or label. Make a note of which number bag goes with which dog. Close the bags.

5 ASK THE SUBJECTS to sniff the socks in all five bags and to name the one they think belongs to their dog.

> **WHAT TO EXPECT** Some people may be better than others at identifying their dogs by smell.

> **WHAT'S GOING ON?** Each individual dog has its smell, and owners may know them by it.

QUESTION THIS!

• Did your results surprise you?

• How could you test your results more widely?

• How could you do this experiment with human smells (that is, your family members)?

DOGS AND POINTING

Can you point out food to your dog?

CONCEPTS

DOMESTICATION, BEHAVIOR

HOW LONG IT TAKES
one day

WHAT YOU NEED
dog treats
two plates
a helper
two to five cups

Humans learn to point by about one year old. Other animals are less likely to respond to pointing. Some captive elephants can, and occasionally cats. But dogs are the champs. They watch humans intently—and have become experts at interpreting our body language. Of course, some dogs are better at this than others.

NOTE ABOUT DUMB DOGS
Dr. Brian Hare says that there are no dumb dogs, just dogs with different learning or behavioral styles. A dog that doesn't look to a person for directions may be better at solving problems for himself.

"Rosie is kind of a genius!"
—Nick

MAKE IT!

1 HAVE YOUR HELPER take your dog six to ten feet (1.8 to 3 m) away from you and have him sit facing you.

2 TAKE TWO TREATS and place them on plates at equal distances from your feet and either side of you, about 24 inches (61 cm) to your left and 24 inches (61 cm) to your right.

3 POINT TO ONE of the treats. Keep your finger pointed at it for the next two steps (4 and 5).

4 NOW SAY "OK." Call your dog and have your helper release him.

5 OBSERVE what happens.

6 LET YOUR DOG have both treats no matter which one he goes to first. (You are not training him, you are checking to see what he knows.)

> **WHAT TO EXPECT** Many dogs will go to the treat you pointed to first.

> **WHAT'S GOING ON?** Scientist Brian Hare says that dogs, like human children and some cats, understand and respond to pointing, realizing that it is designed to communicate information they need. Chimpanzees and wolves can't do this, so Hare thinks the ability is something that developed when dogs (and cats) were domesticated.

QUESTION THIS!

• Which remember where food is for a longer time, cats or dogs? How could you test this?

• Why do dogs and humans respond to pointing, but not chimps and wolves?

• Does this work with puppies or just adult dogs?

BONUS

a. With your dog in another room, hide a treat under one of two to five cups. When the dog comes in, point to the cup with the treat. How does your dog respond?

b. Let your dog watch you put the treat under a cup. Release her while pointing to the cup with the treat. How does your dog respond?

c. Let your dog watch you put the treat under a cup. Release her while pointing to a cup that doesn't have a treat. Which does your dog rely on more—her memory or your gesture?

CAT IQ TEST

Can your cat solve this problem?

CONCEPTS

BEHAVIOR, INTELLIGENCE, CAUSE AND EFFECT

>>> HOW LONG IT TAKES

two hours, including assembly time
(If you use more cats, factor in about
twenty minutes per cat.)

>>> WHAT YOU NEED

large box lid
screen mesh to fit the lid
craft tape or duct tape
scissors or a box cutter
two plastic spoons
string or plastic ties about 12 inches
(30.5 cm) long
small cat treats or cat food
a cat or two or more

Here's one idea for checking a cat's IQ. Try this one—or make up your own puzzle for a cat to solve. A caution: A cat that doesn't pass your test may not be dumb. What else might be going on?

WHAT TO DO

1 MAKE THE TESTING apparatus.

a. Use the scissors or box cutter to cut a window out of the lid of the box. Cover the window with the mesh. This allows the cats to see in.

b. From one end of the box, cut a section out of the edge to allow the string and spoons to extend underneath.

2 TIE THE STRING or plastic ties to the spoon handles.

3 FILL THE SPOONS with cat food or treats and set them under the window so they are visible, with the ends of the strings or ties extending through the hole in the edge and beyond, on the floor.

4 BRING A CAT to the apparatus and let him explore. Observe the cat.

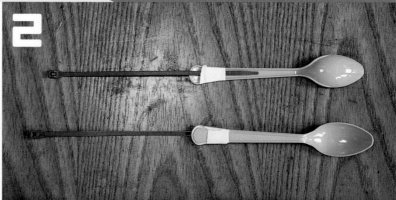

WHAT TO EXPECT Some cats will make the connection between the treat they can see and the string or tie that is attached to it, and they will paw or pull at the tie to get the treat. But others may not figure it out at all—and certain cats will only figure it out some of the time.

WHAT'S GOING ON? To solve this problem, the cat needs to be able to make the connection between the treat he can see, the string that is attached to the spoon holding the treat, and the end of the string that he can see outside the box. Then he needs to figure out that pulling the string will move the treat—and how to pull it so that he can get a hold of it.

FAIL! It was hard to get cats to pay attention to this test. Taegu wouldn't come near the test at all. Olive checked it out, sniffing all around, but didn't try to interact with it. Jack pressed down on the screen and licked the food through it. Our conclusions: Maybe your cat has to be hungry when he takes this test in order to give results. Or maybe this test only looks at one way of solving the problem of getting the food—moving the ties and spoons.

"Jack isn't used to wet food, maybe that's why he tried to go through the screen to get it. But he's a good boy anyway."
—Jen

"See if he'll eat an ant."
—Mae

QUESTION THIS!

• Is this experiment a good indicator of cat intelligence? Why or why not?

• Is there another problem that might be a better indicator of how smart a cat is?

• Would this test be a good indicator of dog or human intelligence? Why or why not?

EGG TRICK

How do eggs react to acid?

REACTION OF CALCIUM CARBONATE TO ACID

HOW LONG IT TAKES
two days

WHAT YOU NEED
two eggs
pot for boiling eggs
water
stove
two glasses or jars to hold the eggs
vinegar
optional: food coloring

4-6

Shells—egg, clam, snail, or whatever—and bones are composed of calcium. They form to give structure and protection to animals. This experiment sheds light on what could happen in the ocean if the trend toward acidification continues. To find out more, Google *ocean acidification*.

WHAT TO DO

DAY ONE:

1 HARD-BOIL ONE EGG.
Place an egg in the pot and cover it with water. With adult assistance, boil it for three minutes, and let it stand for five minutes. Drain and cool.

GLITCH? If boiling cracks your egg's shell, eat this one and boil another. You don't want any cracks in the shell for this experiment.

2 PLACE EACH EGG in a glass or jar. Label the glass to help you remember which egg is hard-boiled and which is raw.

3 POUR VINEGAR into the glasses to cover the eggs. If you want, add food coloring to the vinegar.

4 OBSERVE the eggs after an hour.

DAY TWO:

5 LET THE EGGS continue to soak in the vinegar for two days. Observe them again.

6 TAKE THE EGGS OUT of the vinegar and rinse them in cold water. What do you observe?

WHAT TO EXPECT Bubbles should form on the outside of the eggs at first. Later the shells on the eggs should form a rubbery skin. One egg will be opaque, and the other will become translucent. One egg will have a stronger outer skin than the other. The size of the eggs may change as the eggshell becomes more eaten away and flexible.

WHAT'S GOING ON? The calcium carbonate in the eggshell is a base. It reacts to the acetic acid in the vinegar by forming carbon dioxide (the bubbles). Here is the chemical reaction: $CaCO_3 + 2H^+ \rightarrow Ca^{+2} + H_2O + CO_2$

BONUS

RUBBER BONES

Clean an uncooked chicken bone and allow it to dry overnight. Test flexibility: bend but don't snap! Place in a jar of white vinegar. Each day for a week, remove the bone and test its flexibility. By the end of the week it should be bendy. This demonstrates how bone matrix (collagen—a protein found in bones—and minerals) is affected by acidic vinegar, which breaks down the minerals, leaving only collagen.

QUESTION THIS!

• Do the eggs move as they go through their reaction? How would you explain this?

• How can you explain the change in size?

DOUBLE BONUS:
EXOSKELETON VS. ENDOSKELETON

> *"Where's the rest of the shell? Ew, what happened to it?"*
> —Aaliyah

Compare the effects of vinegar on other body parts, including exoskeleton and endoskeleton: fish bones, eggshells, crab claws, shrimp shells, snail shells, fingernail clippings, teeth . . .

OUR TRY

We used pairs of clam, mussel, crab, oyster, and snail shells from the beach. Most of the shells became soft and flexible, losing their brittleness and in some cases a brittle layer or two. The snail shell underwent the most dramatic change, so that at the end it looked like it had been naturally broken and worn away to start. But it had been shiny and intact just like the control that wasn't soaked in vinegar. In this photo, Aaliyah is looking at what's left of a blue mussel shell.

MAKE FOOTPRINT CASTS

Preserve a footprint to help with identification.

> ### HOW LONG IT TAKES
> an hour, not including the time it takes you to find a print

> ### WHAT YOU NEED
> casting material (plaster of paris or dental stone, one pound per casting)
> water
> three plastic containers, one containing plaster of paris, another containing water, and the third empty
> plastic measuring cup
> plastic spoon or chopstick for stirring
> sturdy shoebox or other container to carry home the cast
> tweezers
> hair spray or spray fixative (from art store)
> optional: a shoulder bag to carry your supplies, a camera

W e left food outside one night, providing coyotes with a midnight snack. How do we know? Big, muddy footprints.

NOTE ABOUT CASTING
This project works great in sand and snow as well as soil. If you're casting in snow, cover the cast with plastic (a plastic bag will do) after pouring the plaster into the print, and leave it 40 to 45 minutes to solidify. With sand and snow, it's simple to just dig out around the cast, and take it along in a crusty pile. Once the plaster is completely firm, you can rinse it to get rid of the sand—and just let the snow melt.

MAKE FOOTPRINT CASTS (CONTINUED)

WHAT TO DO

1 MAKE YOUR OWN footprint or find a print left behind by an animal.

2 TAKE A PHOTOGRAPH of the print. (This is optional, but it provides additional information.)

3 USE TWEEZERS to carefully remove leaves, bugs, stones, and other objects from the imprint. Then spray hair spray or fixative on the print.

4 MIX YOUR CASTING material as directed on its container. For instance, my plaster of paris required two parts of plaster to one part water (for example, two cups [.5 L] of plaster of paris and one cup of water [.25 L]). You want the casting material to have the consistency of a thick milkshake or cake batter.

5 POUR THE CASTING material into the imprint from one side, so that it fills the imprint gradually. Use the spoon to smooth it.

6 LET THE CAST SET for 20 minutes or more. The colder it is outside, the longer you should let the cast set.

7 REMOVE THE CAST by digging the entire impression out with your fingers. You're going to get dirty, but this is the only way to be sure you're picking up the cast in one piece. Place it in the shoebox.

8 LET THE CAST DRY overnight so that it is completely firm inside and out.

GLITCH?
• If your cast breaks in half or a chunk falls off while you're removing it from the print, don't freak out. You can glue it together once it's fully dry, using white glue. But if it crumbles completely, start over, and add a little more casting material to the water to make the cast more solid, or let it set a bit longer until it seems more solid.
• If there's dirt all over your cast, rinse it gently in cold water, and brush out the nooks and crannies with a soft paint brush.

WHAT TO EXPECT Your casting will help you to perceive details about the print that might not be visible otherwise.

WHAT'S GOING ON? The casting material sinks into the nooks and crannies of the impression and brings out details that you can use for animal identification.

OUR TRY
After the coyotes visited, our dogs took a good sniff around the barn. The coyotes had been in a hurry, and they had been wrestling with the food, so we found only partial or messed-up footprints. But the sniffing dogs moved slowly and carefully, not sure what their noses were telling them, and leaving some good impressions in the mud. But whose pawprint was our cast? We matched the cast to our dogs' paws, and then to the culprit: neighbor dog Truffles!

5

7

8

BONUS:
REVERSE PRINT

Once your cast is hard and dry, you can "walk" it into clay or wet sand to replicate the original footprint.

QUESTION THIS!

• What does an impression of a footprint show you that you wouldn't realize otherwise?

"Truffles, why didn't you scare away the coyotes?"
—me

21

NEARSIGHTED HOOPS

Are your hoops skills better with or without your glasses?

CONCEPTS

SCIENTIFIC PROCESS, CONTROLLING VARIABLES

HOW LONG IT TAKES
a day or two, or longer for more data

WHAT YOU NEED
a basketball hoop
chalk
your glasses
a notebook (or a partner with a notebook)

Vision issues can affect your depth perception, an important factor in the eye-hand coordination you need to shoot a basket. You may assume you're better with or without your glasses. Find out what the real story is, as Nikitha and Justin did.

WHAT TO DO

1 DETERMINE THREE positions from which you will shoot, and use chalk to mark them on your court or driveway with a number or letter.

2 TAKE THE SAME number of shots with and without your glasses from each position, and record the number of shots and baskets.

NOTE ABOUT THE SCIENTIFIC METHOD Each time you test yourself, take shots in the same order, at the same time of the day. Record the weather conditions and how you feel, but try to keep every other variable consistent. That is, if you try jump shots from one position, try them from the others. Shoot the same way with and without your glasses.

3 ANALYZE YOUR DATA. Figure out your shot percentage (number of baskets divided by number of shots for each condition and position, multiplied by 100).

4 GRAPH YOUR DATA to create an easy visualization of your results.

WHAT TO EXPECT Your results will vary depending on your vision and your ability to compensate for it.

"I'm definitely better with my glasses on."
—Justin

QUESTION THIS!

- How can you explain your results?

- Are you surprised by your results?

CREDITS

Acknowledgments

Our Models, **Humans**: Aaliyah, Abigail, Adriana, Allison, Ariel, Bailey, Brandon, Caitlyn, Cole, Doug, Dylan, Emily, Isaac, Janelle, Jarrett, Jason, Jen, Justin, Lori, Luke, Mae, Marco, Nick, Nikitha, Niyanna, Patsy, Priyanka, Serenity, Sossi, Stephanie, Trijon, Wyatt; **Pets**: Jen's and Mae's cats: Jack and Olive; Karen's cat: Taegu; Karen's dogs: Cherubino and Rosamund; Michael's dog: Truffles

Special thanks to Tina Kiniry at the John Casablancas Modeling Agency

All photographs shot on location by Matthew Rakola

Published by the National Geographic Society

John M. Fahey, *Chairman of the Board and Chief Executive Officer*
Declan Moore, *Executive Vice President; President, Publishing and Travel*
Melina Gerosa Bellows, *Executive Vice President; Chief Creative Officer, Books, Kids, and Family*

Prepared by the Book Division

Hector Sierra, *Senior Vice President and General Manager*
Nancy Laties Feresten, *Senior Vice President, Kids Publishing and Media*
Jennifer Emmett, *Vice President, Editorial Director, Kids Books*
Eva Absher-Schantz, *Design Director, Kids Publishing and Media*
Jay Sumner, *Director of Photography, Kids Publishing and Media*
R. Gary Colbert, *Production Director*
Jennifer A. Thornton, *Director of Managing Editorial*

Staff for This Book

Priyanka Lamichhane, *Project Editor*
Angela Modany, *Assistant Editor*
Eva Absher-Schantz, *Art Director*
Lori Epstein, *Senior Photo Editor*
Itzhack Shelomi, *Designer*
Ariane Szu-Tu, *Editorial Assistant*
Paige Towler, *Editorial Intern*
Sanjida Rashid and Rachel Kenny, *Design Production Assistants*
Margaret Leist, *Photo Assistant*
Grace Hill, *Associate Managing Editor*
Joan Gossett, *Production Editor*
Lewis R. Bassford, *Production Manager*
Susan Borke, *Legal and Business Affairs*

Production Services

Phillip L. Schlosser, *Senior Vice President*
Chris Brown, *Vice President, NG Book Manufacturing*
George Bounelis, *Senior Production Manager*
Nicole Elliott, *Director of Production*
Rachel Faulise, *Manager*
Robert L. Barr, *Manager*

The National Geographic Society is one of the world's largest nonprofit scientific and educational organizations. Founded in 1888 to "increase and diffuse geographic knowledge," the Society's mission is to inspire people to care about the planet. It reaches more than 400 million people worldwide each month through its official journal, *National Geographic*, and other magazines; National Geographic Channel; television documentaries; music; radio; films; books; DVDs; maps; exhibitions; live events; school publishing programs; interactive media; and merchandise. National Geographic has funded more than 10,000 scientific research, conservation and exploration projects and supports an education program promoting geographic literacy.

For more information, please visit nationalgeographic.com, call 1-800-NGS LINE (647-5463), or write to the following address:
National Geographic Society
1145 17th Street N.W.
Washington, D.C. 20036-4688 U.S.A.

Visit us online at nationalgeographic.com/books

For librarians and teachers: ngchildrensbooks.org

More for kids from National Geographic:
kids.nationalgeographic.com

For information about special discounts for bulk purchases, please contact National Geographic Books Special Sales: ngspecsales@ngs.org

For rights or permissions inquiries, please contact National Geographic Books Subsidiary Rights: ngbookrights@ngs.org

Dollar Tree edition ISBN: 978-1-4263-2379-9

Printed in the U.S.A.
15/KG/1